Lake Press Pty Ltd
5 Burwood Road
Hawthorn VIC 3122 Australia
Email: publishing@lakepress.com.au
www.lakepress.com.au

First published 2018
Printed by Great Dragon Printing and Graphic Co Ltd
Manufactured and printed in Guangdong Province, China
Second printing September 2018 5 4 3 2
LP19 044

M!NDGAMES

TRUE or FALSE?

LAKE PRESS

Contents

1. Dogs sweat through their saliva.

2. Cats have whiskers on their legs.

3. Rabbits are born blind.

4. There's a species of sea animal called the bone-eating snot flower.

5. Sharks are color blind.

6. Whales have belly buttons.

7. Tarantulas turn their prey into liquid and drink it.

8. The world's most venomous spider is the tarantula.

9. Most spiders make silk to create their webs.

10. The tiger is the largest living land carnivore.

11. It's the male lion that does most of the hunting.

12. Spotted hyenas have teeth strong enough to crush bones.

13. Pandas are herbivores.

14. *Koalas eat poisonous leaves.*

15. Sloths can't swim.

16. Elephants are the second-largest land animal in the world.

17. Kangaroos can't walk backwards.

18. Gorillas can use sign language.

19. Hummingbirds can fly backwards.

20. Ostriches are the fastest runners in the world.

21. A group of crows is called a flap.

**22. Most snakes in the world
are venomous.**

*23. Crocodiles swallow small
stones to help digest their food.*

**24. A turtle's gender depends on how warm
or cold it is while it's still in its egg.**

25. Bees produce honey for their food during winter.

26. There are around 1.4 million ants in the world.

27. Dung beetles are very fragile insects.

28. A giraffe's spots are there for camouflage.

29. Female dolphins are called does.

30. Frogs don't drink water.

31. Cheetahs can't roar.

32. Wolves must eat every day in order to stay alive.

33. The rhinoceros horn is made of cartilage.

Answers

1. **False.** *Amazingly, they actually sweat through the pads of their paws.*
2. **True.** *Cats have whiskers on their front legs to help them navigate in the dark and work out the width of gaps.*
3. **True.** *They are also born deaf and without fur on their bodies.*
4. **True.** *This recently discovered species that looks like a worm is found in the North Sea. Its scientific name translates to 'bone-eating snot flower'.*
5. **False.** *A lot of sharks have very good eyesight.*
6. **True.** *Whales are mammals like humans – their babies are attached to the mother via an umbilical cord in the same way, which creates a belly button when it detaches after birth.*
7. **True.** *Tarantulas have a straw-like mouth, which they use to drink their prey!*

8. **False.** *The world's most venomous spider is the Sydney funnel-web spider, which is found in Australia.*

9. **True.** *They spin silk from their spinnerets to make the webs that catch their prey.*

10. **False.** *Polar bears are the largest land carnivore.*

11. **False.** *Female lions are the hunters!*

12. **True.** *Hyenas crush and eat the bones of their prey to get the marrow, which is very nutritious.*

13. **False.** *Although a panda's diet is 99% bamboo, they sometimes eat small animals or birds, making them omnivores.*

14. **True!** *Koalas have a long digestive organ called a cecum that breaks down eucalyptus leaves so their poison won't harm the animal.*

15. **False.** *Sloths are slow and clumsy on land, but they are great swimmers.*

16. **False.** *They're actually the largest!*

17. **True.** *Their thick tail stops them from being able to walk backwards.*

Answers

18. **True.** *Gorillas are very intelligent and have been taught to use sign language in captivity. One gorilla, Koko, was taught around 1000 signs and understood around 2000 English words.*
19. **True.** *Hummingbirds are the only birds that can fly backwards.*
20. **True.** *Ostriches can run at more than 43 miles (70 km) per hour. They're also the world's largest bird.*
21. **False.** *A group of crows is called a murder!*
22. **False.** *Out of about 3000, only about 500 snake species are venomous, and only around 30–40 are considered harmful to humans.*
23. **True.** *The small stones grind up the food in crocodiles' stomachs.*
24. **True.** *Warm temperatures mean the baby turtle is more likely to be female, and cool temperatures mean the baby is more likely to be male.*

25. **True.** *Bees make much more honey than they need, though, so we get to have the leftovers.*

26. **False.** *In fact, it's been estimated that there are around 1.4 million ants for every human (based on a population of 7.3 billion people) – that's 10 quadrillion ants!*

27. **False.** *A dung beetle can drag 1141 times its weight – the same as a human dragging six double-decker buses!*

28. **True.** *The spots on a giraffe's fur camouflage them to protect them from predators when they stand among trees.*

29. **False.** *They're called cows.*

30. **True.** *Instead of drinking water, frogs absorb it into their body through their skin.*

31. **True.** *Cheetahs do purr, though.*

32. **False.** *Wolves in the Arctic, where it's very cold, take longer to find food and sometimes go for several days without eating.*

33. **False.** *Its horn is actually made from compacted hair!*

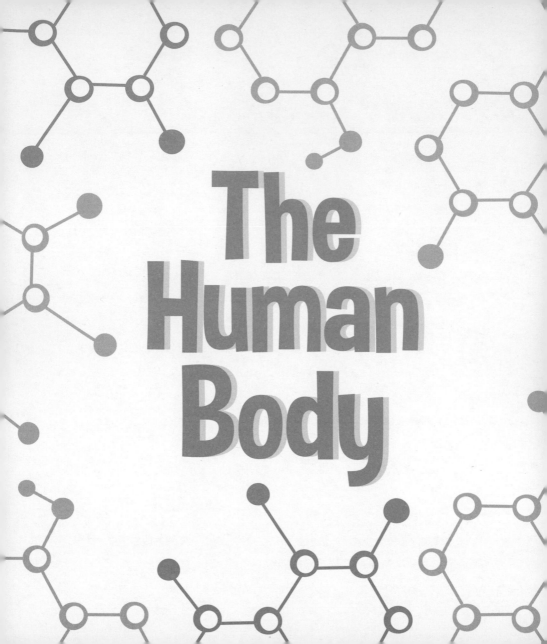

The Human Body

1. Your stomach acid can dissolve metal.

2. You're taller in the morning than in the evening.

3. Although you have a unique fingerprint, your toe print isn't unique.

4. In your lifetime, your mouth produces enough saliva to fill two medium-size bathtubs, on average.

5. Sticking out your tongue is considered rude all over the world.

6. Humans share more than 50% of our DNA with bananas.

7. Your ears and nose have finished growing by the time you're 18.

8. The human body is around 60% water.

9. Without a stomach, you would die.

10. Around 50% of your hand strength comes from your pinky finger.

11. *Your heart is protected by your rib cage.*

12. The ear's only function is to help you hear.

13. The left side of the brain controls the right side of the body, and the right side of the brain controls the left side.

14. Your thigh is the strongest muscle in your body.

15. Your two lungs are exactly the same size.

16. Human teeth are as strong as shark teeth.

17. *Babies can't make tears until they're at least one month old.*

18. Ear wax is bad for your ears.

19. Your brain does not feel pain.

20. The tallest person to ever live was nearly 9 feet, or 3 metres, tall.

21. Your skeleton does not change through your whole life.

22. Humans have five senses: sight, hearing, taste, touch and smell.

23. Human noses can recognize a million different scents.

24. The average person walks the equivalent of five times around the world in a lifetime.

25. Humans are the only species known to blush.

26. The human body has around 200 muscles.

27. The smallest bone in your body is in your pinky toe.

Answers

1. **True.** *Your body is safe from the acid, though, because your stomach cells are replaced faster than the stomach acid can destroy them!*

2. **True.** *You're tallest when you first get out of bed; by the evening, the discs in your back have been compressed from standing all day, so you're slightly shorter by bedtime (around half an inch, or 1 cm).*

3. **False.** *Just like fingerprints, no-one else has the same toe print as you. We also have unique tongue prints.*

4. **False.** *It would fill around 53 bathtubs!*

5. **False.** *In a lot of countries sticking your tongue out at someone is considered rude, but in Tibet it's a greeting.*

6. **True.** *We share the same genes that are needed for cells to function.*

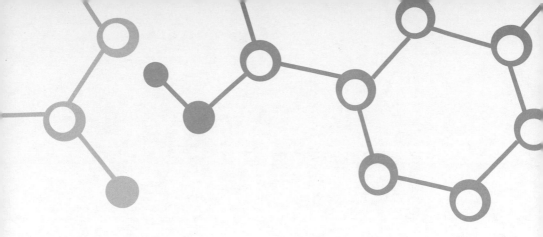

7. **False.** *They don't stop growing until you die.*
8. **True.** *We're mostly water!*
9. **False.** *You can live without a stomach. If you have a medical reason for having your stomach removed, your esophagus will be joined to your small intestine and food will travel through your body quicker.*
10. **True.** *If you lose your pinky finger, your hand strength will be cut by half.*
11. **True.** *Your heart is tucked safely behind your rib cage.*
12. **False.** *Your inner ear contains fluid that moves when you move, sending your brain signals and keeping you balanced.*
13. **True.** *Scientists don't yet understand why.*
14. **False.** *Your strongest muscle is the masseter, in your jaw.*
15. **False.** *Your left lung is around 10% smaller than your right one, to allow room for your heart.*
16. **True.** *It's the way sharks feed that makes it appear as though their teeth are tougher.*

Answers

17. **True.** *They can cry from the moment they're born, but there are no tears for a month or so.*
18. **False.** *Ear wax helps to protect the ear by stopping dirt and dust from getting to your inner ear.*
19. **True.** *Even though the brain processes pain signals, it doesn't have pain receptors so it doesn't feel pain itself.*
20. **True.** *The Guinness World Record holder for the tallest person ever is Robert Pershing Wadlow, who was born in the USA in 1918. He was 8 feet 11 inches (2.72 metres) tall.*
21. **False.** *It actually renews itself completely every 10 years!*

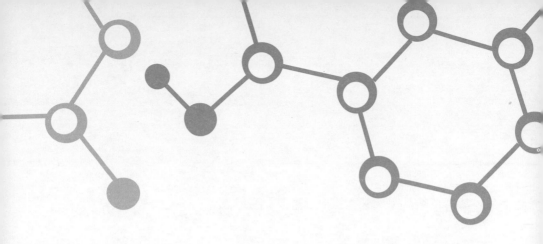

22. **True.** *Although many scientists think there are more, it's generally agreed that these are the five main senses.*
23. **False.** *Scientists think that the nose can recognize a trillion different scents!*
24. **True.** *We take on average around 7500 steps per day, or around 216,262,500 steps over a lifetime.*
25. **True.** *It seems that apes and other primates don't blush. Nor do other animals. When you blush, so does the lining of your stomach!*
26. **False.** *There are more than 600 muscles in your body. We use around 200 of them to take a single step.*
27. **False.** *It's in your ear; it's called the stapes.*

Movies &
Television

1. The quote 'May the Force be with you' is from the movie *Star Trek*.

2. The name of the main character in Riverdale *is* Archie Anderson.

3. There are seven *Harry Potter* books but eight movies.

4. In the TV series *A Series of Unfortunate Events*, the siblings are Violet, Karl and Sandy Baudelaire.

5. The Hunger Games *movies are based on a series of novels.*

6. Edward Cullen from the *Twilight* movies was a vampire.

7. Will Byers disappears in the series *Stranger Things*.

8. Leonardo DiCaprio was the lead male actor in the movie Titanic.

9.The Wicked Witch of the West died at the beginning of *The Wizard of Oz*.

10. In the movie *Divergent*, people are divided into factions according to human virtues.

11. In ET the Extra-Terrestrial, *Elliot discovers ET in his back yard.*

12. In the movie *Beauty and the Beast*, Belle is played by Emma Watson.

13. In *Coco*, Miguel accidentally gets stuck in the land of the living.

14. The main character in the movie Elf, Buddy, grew up in New York and as an adult decides to move to the North Pole and become an elf.

15. In the movie *Gremlins*, Gizmo the mogwai must be fed after midnight.

16. The main character in the movie *Fantastic Beasts and Where to Find Them* is Harry Potter.

17. Jack Black pretends to be a teacher who puts together a school band in School of Rock.

18. The movie *Freaky Friday* is about a teenage girl, Anna, who turns into her brother one night.

19. In *The Avengers: Infinity War*, the Avengers team up with Batman.

20. The series Once Upon a Time *includes characters from many different fairy tales.*

21. In the movie *High School Musical*, Troy and Gabriella try out for the school musical.

22. In the movie *Arrival*, the main character travels to another planet to communicate with aliens.

23. Hazel and Gus, the two main characters in The Fault in Our Stars, *both have asthma.*

24. The movie *Jurassic World* is set at a luxury resort where genetically engineered dinosaurs live.

25. The movie *Pitch Perfect* revolves around a group of dancers.

26. The series The 100 is set 97 years after civilization on Earth has been all but destroyed by a nuclear holocaust.

27. Buffy Summers, the main character in *Buffy the Vampire Slayer*, battles vampires and demons.

28. The latest actor to play *Doctor Who* in the TV series is a woman.

29. Lorelai and Rory are sisters in Gilmore Girls.

30. In the animated TV series *The Simpsons*, Homer works at the Springfield Nuclear Power Plant.

31. *Elementary* **is a TV series based on Sherlock Holmes.**

32. Two of the main characters in the series Modern Family *are Claire and Greg Dunphy.*

33. The series *The Vampire Diaries* **is set in Vampire Falls.**

Answers

1. **False.** *It's from the Star Wars movies.*
2. **False.** *His name is Archie Andrews.*
3. **True.** *The final book, Harry Potter and the Deathly Hallows, was made into two movies.*
4. **False.** *Their names are Violet, Klaus and Sunny.*
5. **True.** *The trilogy of books are The Hunger Games, Catching Fire and Mockingjay.*
6. **True.** *Edward was played by the actor Robert Pattinson.*
7. **True.** *Will is abducted and his friends Dustin, Lucas and Mike try to solve the mystery of his disappearance.*
8. **True.** *He played Jack, and Kate Winslet played Rose.*
9. **False.** *It was the Wicked Witch of the East who was squashed under Dorothy's house when it landed in Oz.*

10. **True.** *The main character, Tris Prior, chooses the Dauntless faction, but is told she is Divergent and cannot fit into any faction.*

11. **True.** *Elliot and his brother and sister try to hide ET from the adults, while helping him devise a plan to go home to his own planet.*

12. **True.** *Emma is otherwise known for playing Hermione in the Harry Potter movies.*

13. **False.** *Miguel finds himself in the land of the dead, where he looks for his great-great-grandfather to try to get home to his family.*

14. **False.** *Buddy was raised as an elf and when he discovers he isn't actually an elf, he heads to New York to find his real father.*

15. **False.** *Billy, his owner, is told he must never expose Gizmo to bright light, never get it wet, and never feed it after midnight.*

16. **False.** *It's Newt Scamander, a wizard and 'magizoologist'.*

17. **True.** *The band performs in the Battle of the Bands at the end of the movie.*

18. **False.** *Anna and her mother accidentally swap bodies.*

Answers

19. **False.** *They join forces with the Guardians of the Galaxy.*

20. **True.** *The main characters include Snow White, Prince Charming and Rumplestiltskin, among others.*

21. **True.** *There are two sequels to the movie.*

22. **False.** *When alien spaceships land in various places around Earth, Louise, who studies languages, is recruited to try to communicate with them.*

23. **False.** *They've both had cancer.*

24. **True.** *When one of the dinosaurs escapes, chaos ensues!*

25. **False.** *The movie follows an acapella singing group called the Barden Bellas, who go to Barden University.*

26. **True.** *A small number of survivors live on The Ark, in Earth's orbit, and 100 teenage prisoners are sent back to Earth to see if the planet has become habitable again.*

27. **True.** *She has a group of friends called the Scooby Gang, or Scoobies, who help her in her quests.*

28. **True.** *The actor Jodie Whittaker plays the 13th and first-ever female Doctor Who in the series.*

29. **False.** *Lorelai is Rory's mother.*

30. **True.** *Homer lives in Springfield with his wife Marge and their kids Bart, Lisa and Maggie.*

31. **True.** *Unlike the original story, though, the series is set in the present day, and Holmes' offsider, Dr Watson, is a woman.*

32. **False.** *Their names are Claire and Phil Dunphy, and their children are Haley, Alex and Luke.*

33. **False.** *It's set in Mystic Falls.*

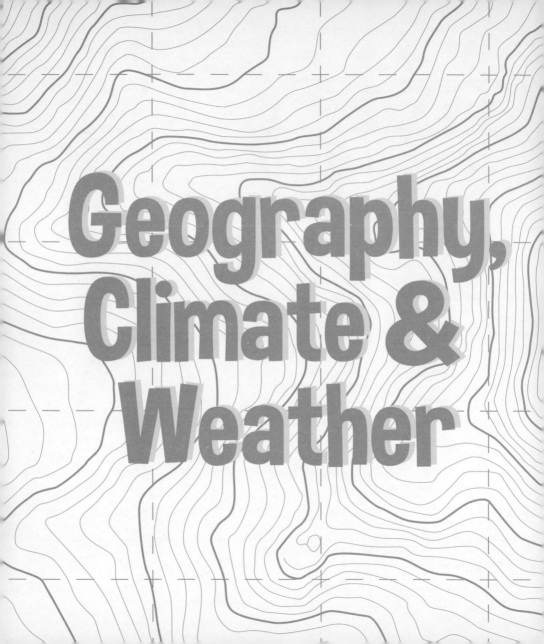

Geography, Climate & Weather

1. The Great Barrier Reef, off the coast of Australia, is the largest living structure on Earth.

2. Antarctica is the largest desert in the world.

3. 'Tsunami' is the Japanese word for a city.

4. The Amazon is the longest river in South America.

5. *Canada is the largest country in the world.*

6. The hottest place in the world is Death Valley, in California, USA.

7. Shanghai in China is the largest city in the world by population.

8. *The highest mountain in the world is Mount Everest, in the Himalayas.*

9. The most famous pyramids in the world are found in Lebanon.

10. Paris is the capital of France.

11. *The South Pole is colder than the North Pole.*

12. The Richter scale measures the age of trees.

13. The five oceans of the world are the Southern, the Pacific, the Atlantic, the Indian and the Arctic.

14. The country Greece is part of Africa.

15. Hurricanes, tropical cyclones and typhoons are all different types of storms.

16. Some parts of land today were underwater in the last Ice Age.

17. *Stalagmites and stalactites are formed on high mountains.*

18. The climate in the Arctic is warm and sunny.

19. The liquid inside a volcano is called magma.

20. Kabul is the capital city of Pakistan.

21. The only two countries that have a land border with the USA are Canada and Mexico.

22. An Indian emperor had the Taj Mahal, a beautiful white marble building in India, built for one of his wives when she died.

23. English is the most spoken language in the world.

24. As our climate gets warmer, our weather will get more unpredictable and we'll have stronger storms.

25. Hawaii has the most volcanoes in the world.

26. Vatican City is the smallest country in the world.

27. The country of Iceland is covered in ice.

Answers

1. **True.** *It's more than 1243 miles (2000 km) long and 217,480 square miles (350,000 square km).*
2. **True.** *It's classed as a desert because it gets so little rain and snow. It rains less there than in the Sahara Desert in North Africa, which is the largest hot desert in the world.*
3. **False.** *A tsunami is a series of huge waves caused by an earthquake.*
4. **True.** *It's at least 4000 miles, or 6400 km, long, and travels through six countries (Peru, Bolivia, Venezuela, Colombia, Ecuador and Brazil).*
5. **False.** *Russia is the largest country.*

6. **True.** *It holds the Guinness World Record for the highest temperature, 134.06 degrees Fahrenheit, or 56.7 degrees Celsius.*

7. **False.** *Tokyo in Japan has the largest population of any city in the world, at around 38 million people.*

8. **True.** *The second-highest is K2, which is also in the Himalayas.*

9. **False.** *They're found in Egypt.*

10. **True.** *It's known as the City of Lights.*

11. **True.** *It's colder than the North Pole because it sits on a very thick ice sheet.*

12. **False.** *It measures the strength of earthquakes.*

Answers

13. **True.** *The largest of the oceans is the Pacific.*
14. **False.** *Greece is part of Europe.*
15. **False.** *They're all the same type of weather system: a very strong storm with high winds and a lot of rain. They're just called different things in different parts of the world.*
16. **False.** *So much water was trapped in ice that the sea levels were much lower than they are now – the equivalent of the height of a 40-story building!*
17. **False.** *They're found in caves.*
18. **False.** *It's cold and windy in the Arctic, where the North Pole is located.*

19. **True.** *Once it's outside the volcano, it's called lava.*
20. **False.** *It's the capital of Afghanistan.*
21. **True.** *Canada is to the north, and Mexico is to the south.*
22. **True.** *The building was completely finished in 1653.*
23. **False.** *It's actually Mandarin Chinese.*
24. **True.** *Warm air holds more moisture, which means heavier rain.*
25. **False.** *It's Indonesia.*
26. **True.** *The home of the Pope is actually a country within Rome, Italy.*
27. **False.** *It's actually quite green; only 11% of the country is covered with permanent ice.*

1. There are five players per team in a basketball game.

2. Muhammad Ali was a world champion runner.

3. Cricket is played at Wimbledon.

4. The flat rubber disc used in ice hockey is called a 'duck'.

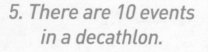

5. There are 10 events in a decathlon.

6. Football, or soccer, is the most popular sport in the world.

7. The word 'love' is a score in tennis.

8. *The Tour de France is a running race.*

9. There are five rings in the Olympic logo.

10. The three sports that are part of the triathlon are swimming, running and cycling.

11. The English rugby union team performs the haka before their matches.

12. There are four holes in a ten-pin bowling ball.

13. Squash is played with a racquet and ball.

14. In shot put, the athlete throws a metal ball attached to a steel wire by holding the wire and swinging the ball around.

15. Polo is a sport played on horseback.

**16. There are four bases
on a baseball field.**

*17. A regular golf
course has 20 holes.*

18. Butterfly is a swimming stroke.

19. The first Olympic Games were first held in ancient Egypt.

20. In badminton, players hit a white ball to each other.

21. The javelin is a long spear that is thrown in an Olympic athletics event.

22. Ian Thorpe has won the most Olympic gold medals ever in swimming.

23. The uneven bars is an apparatus used in gymnastics.

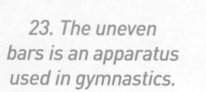

24. In the pole vault, athletes use a long pole to help them jump over a high bar.

25. The sport of volleyball is held in a velodrome.

26. Argentina has won the most football (soccer) World Cups.

27. The approved color of a tennis ball is yellow.

28. In a cricket Test match, two teams might play for five days and there still might not be a winner.

29. Wing attack is a basketball position.

30. If you're an expert in many kinds of martial arts, you wear a black belt.

31. A slam dunk is something you do in long jump.

32. The person sitting in the chair overseeing a tennis match is called a referee.

33. You can get a hole in one in golf.

Answers

1. **True.** *Five players from each team are allowed on the court at one time.*

2. **False.** *He was a world champion boxer.*

3. **False.** *Tennis is played at Wimbledon; it's one of four Grand Slam events held every year.*

4. **False.** *It's called a puck.*

5. **True.** *The events are the 100 m run, long jump, shot put, high jump, 400 m run, 110 m hurdles, discus, pole vault, javelin and 1500 m run.*

6. **True.** *It's estimated that more than half of the world's population are football (soccer) fans.*

7. **True.** *A score of love means the player has not won any points in a game yet.*

8. **False.** *It's a bicycle race.*

9. **True.** *The rings are blue, yellow, black, green and red.*

10. **True.** *The swimming leg is first, followed by the cycling and finishing with the running.*
11. **False.** *New Zealand's rugby team, the All Blacks, performs the haka, a traditional war dance.*
12. **False.** *There are three holes.*
13. **True.** *It's played in a four-walled court with a rubber ball.*
14. **False.** *The athlete throws a heavy metal ball by 'pushing' it as far as possible.*
15. **True.** *Players try to score goals by hitting a small white ball along the ground with a long-handled mallet.*
16. **True.** *They are home plate, first base, second base and third base.*
17. **False.** *It has 18 holes.*
18. **True.** *It gets its name from the movements the swimmer's arms make, which look a little like two wings moving through the water.*

Answers

19. **False.** *They were first held in Olympia, Greece, in 776 BC. The first modern Olympic Games were held in Athens, Greece in 1896.*

20. **False.** *They hit a shuttlecock.*

21. **True.** *The athlete who throws the spear the furthest wins.*

22. **False.** *Michael Phelps has won the most Olympic gold medals in swimming, with 23 gold.*

23. **True.** *The gymnast performs a routine on two horizontal bars, set at different heights.*

24. **True.** *The pole is flexible and bends when the athlete pushes the end of it into the ground to help them get over the pole.*

25. **False.** *Cycling events are held in a velodrome; there are also road races.*

26. **False.** *Brazil has won the most World Cups, with five wins.*
27. **True.** *A lot of people think it's green, but the color approved by the International Tennis Federation is a fluorescent yellow called 'optic yellow'. White balls can also be used.*
28. **True.** *Test matches last between three and five days, with no guarantee of a winner!*
29. **False.** *Wing attack is a netball position.*
30. **True.** *In martial arts like karate, getting a black belt means you're an expert.*
31. **False.** *In basketball, a slam dunk is when a player jumps up and slams the ball down through the basket.*
32. **False.** *They're called umpires.*
33. **True.** *You get a hole in one when you hit the ball off the tee and it goes into the hole without you having to hit it again.*

SPACE

ANSWERS ON PAGE 92

1. Saturn and Jupiter are the only planets with rings.

2. Humans have not yet landed on Mars.

3. The Hubble Space Telescope is the name of NASA's famous space telescope.

4. The closest planet to the sun is Mars.

5. Our galaxy is called the Milky Road.

6. The hottest planet in our solar system is Venus.

7. Earth orbits the moon.

8. The planet in our solar system with the most moons is Neptune.

9. Gravity is what allows us to travel into space.

10. The sun will run out of energy in around 5 billion years.

11. Humans can breathe on the moon.

12. The first person to walk on the moon was Neil Armstrong.

13. An observatory is a place that uses telescopes and other scientific equipment to research space.

14. Mars is known as the red planet because it is covered in dark-red dust.

15. A lunar eclipse is when the moon moves between the sun and Earth, blocking our view of the sun.

16. An astronomer is a scientist who studies space.

17. Pluto is the ninth planet in our solar system.

18. The Big Bang Theory is a theory that explains the beginning of the universe.

19. The sun rises in the west.

20. *The sun is a star.*

21. There are eight planets in our solar system.

22. Earth is sometimes called the green planet.

23. A black hole allows you to travel through space.

24. NASA is the famous United States government agency that runs the US space program.

**25. It takes 28 days for Earth
to travel around the sun.**

*26. Meteorites crash into the moon,
causing lots of craters.*

**27. People live on the
International Space Station.**

Answers

1. **False.** *Neptune and Uranus also have rings.*
2. **True.** *It's predicted that we will in the next 50 years, though.*
3. **True.** *In space, the telescope can see much further into the universe than it could on Earth.*
4. **False.** *Mercury is the closest planet to the sun.*
5. **False.** *It's called the Milky Way.*
6. **True.** *Although Venus isn't the closest planet to the sun, its temperature is hotter because it has thick clouds made up of mostly carbon dioxide, which is a greenhouse gas that makes the planet hotter.*
7. **False.** *Earth orbits the sun.*
8. **False.** *Jupiter has the most moons, with 63 at last count.*
9. **False.** *Gravity is the force that holds us to Earth.*

10. **True.** *If humans are still around then, they'll have to find another planet to live on!*

11. **False.** *Humans can't breathe normally in space the way they can on Earth. There's no oxygen in space, and we need to breathe oxygen to keep us alive.*

12. **True.** *He was part of Apollo 11, the first mission to land on the moon in 1969.*

13. **True.** *They're usually built in remote places, away from the lights of civilization, so their telescopes can see into space more clearly.*

14. **True.** *The red dust comes from the iron in the planet's surface.*

15. **False.** *That's a solar eclipse. A lunar eclipse happens when Earth moves between the sun and the moon, which stops the sun from reflecting off the moon.*

Answers

16. **True.** *They study planets and the sun in our solar system, as well as other parts of the universe.*
17. **False.** *Before 2006 Pluto was considered a planet, but in 2006 scientists decided it is instead a dwarf planet.*
18. **True.** *The Big Bang Theory is the theory that the universe began billions of years ago as a small, dense ball of energy, and that ball blew up and expanded into the universe.*
19. **False.** *It rises in the east. It doesn't actually move at all, though – it appears that way because Earth is rotating around it.*
20. **True.** *The sun is a huge ball of gas, made up of mostly hydrogen and a bit of helium.*

21. **True.** *They are Mercury, Venus, Earth, Mars, Jupiter, Saturn, Uranus and Neptune.*
22. **False.** *It's sometimes called the blue planet, because 70% of its surface is covered by water so it looks mostly blue from space.*
23. **False.** *A black hole is sometimes made in the place of a star that has died. Gravity in a black hole is so strong that not even light can escape it.*
24. **True.** *NASA stands for National Aeronautics and Space Administration.*
25. **False.** *It takes one year, or 365 days, for Earth to travel around the sun.*
26. **True.** *The moon is constantly hit by meteorites and other objects.*
27. **True.** *The International Space Station (ISS) orbits around Earth. The people on the ISS study space and perform experiments to help us understand space and how we relate to it.*

1. The rice dish priella comes from Spain.

2. Pizza is a food that comes from Italy.

3. Humans are omnivores.

4. Avocados are used to make guacamole.

5. Brazil is the world's largest producer of bananas.

**6. Lures, rods, hooks and baits are
used to farm sheep.**

7. Dairy products are needed for healthy bones and teeth.

8. Carrots aren't only orange.

9. A tomato is a vegetable.

10. In France, some people eat frogs' legs and snails.

11. Grapes grow on trees.

12. Lamingtons are cakes covered in desiccated coconut.

13. Spinach is good for you because it's full of carbohydrates.

14. You can drink coconut milk straight from a coconut.

15. Cutting onions can make you cry.

16. Some people like putting fish on their pizza.

17. Neapolitan ice-cream is another name for chocolate fudge ice-cream.

18. Sugar is the ingredient that makes bread rise.

19. Potatoes grow on small plants near the ground.

20. Shiitake is a kind of mushroom.

21. Calamari is a Greek dish, which is beef.

22. Fajitas are eaten a lot in Mexico.

23. Brussels sprouts look like baby cabbages.

24. Offal, the internal organs and other normally unused parts of an animal, is eaten in some parts of the world.

25. Golden Delicious is a brand of orange.

26. Currants and sultanas are dried grapes.

27. Nori, the dark-green that's wrapped around sushi, is made from seaweed.

**28. Someone who doesn't eat meat
is called a vegan.**

29. The main ingredient of black pudding is blood.

30. Chocolate comes from the cacao tree.

31. Foods like pasta and bread are classed as high in fructose.

32. Roquefort is a kind of cheese.

33. Watermelon is considered the sweetest fruit in the world.

1. **False.** *The dish is called paella.*
2. **True.** *It's thought to have come from Naples in Italy.*
3. **True.** *We eat meat and plant foods like vegetables and fruit.*
4. **True.** *Guacamole comes from Mexico but is popular throughout the world.*
5. **False.** *India produces the most bananas.*
6. **False.** *They're used in fishing.*
7. **True.** *The calcium in dairy products is what's good for your bones and teeth.*
8. **True.** *You can get yellow, purple, white and red ones too.*
9. **False.** *Tomatoes are a fruit.*
10. **True.** *They're considered a delicacy.*

Answers

11. **False.** *They grow on vines, and can be red, black/purple or green.*
12. **True.** *Originating in Australia, they're made with sponge cake, coated in chocolate and rolled in coconut.*
13. **False.** *Spinach has lots of iron in it, so it's good for building strong muscles.*
14. **False.** *Coconut water is found inside a coconut – that's the liquid you can drink straight from a coconut. Coconut milk is what you get when you crush the white coconut flesh.*
15. **True.** *There's a chemical in them that makes your eyes create tears.*
16. **True.** *A small, salty fish called an anchovy is a common pizza ingredient.*

17. **False.** *Neapolitan ice-cream combines chocolate, vanilla and strawberry ice cream.*

18. **False.** *It's yeast that makes bread rise.*

19. **False.** *Potatoes grow under the ground.*

20. **True.** *The shiitake mushroom comes from Japan.*

21. **False.** *It's squid!*

22. **True.** *They're grilled meat and vegetables in a soft tortilla.*

23. **True.** *They are actually part of the cabbage family.*

24. **True.** *It includes things like brains, liver, kidneys, tongue and pigs' trotters!*

25. **False.** *It's a type of apple.*

Answers

26. **True.** *Currants are dried black grapes, and sultanas are dried white grapes.*
27. **True.** *Nori is dried sheets of seaweed.*
28. **False.** *Vegetarians don't eat meat; vegans don't eat meat or any animal products, like milk or eggs, either.*
29. **True.** *It's commonly eaten in Britain.*
30. **True.** *It comes from the cacao beans that grow on the tree.*
31. **False.** *They're high in carbohydrates.*
32. **True.** *It's a sheep milk cheese that comes from France.*
33. **False.** *The mango is considered the sweetest.*

1. There were five band members in One Direction.

2. Demi Lovato had a hit song 'Sorry Not Sorry'.

**3. One of the members of
5 Seconds of Summer is named Duke.**

4. Meghan Trainor released the album *No Thanks* in 2016.

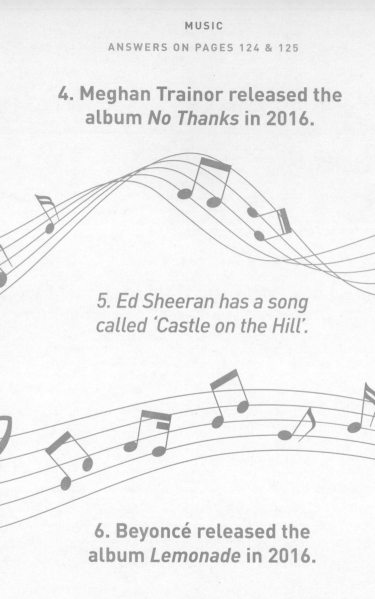

5. Ed Sheeran has a song called 'Castle on the Hill'.

6. Beyoncé released the album *Lemonade* in 2016.

7. One of Bruno Mars' most popular songs is 'Downtown Funk'.

8. The first line in the Harry Styles song 'Sign of the Times' is 'Gotta get away from here'.

9. Shawn Mendes is from Canada.

10. Lady Gaga's real first name is Greta.

*11. Drake released the song
'My Plan' in 2018.*

12. Sia is Australian.

**13. Eminem sang the song 'Can't Stop the Feeling',
which was in the movie *Trolls*.**

14. Little Mix released the song 'Power' in 2010.

**15. The Rita Ora song 'Anywhere'
includes the lyrics 'A million miles from LA'.**

16. Ariana Grande released the album
Dangerous Woman **in 2016.**

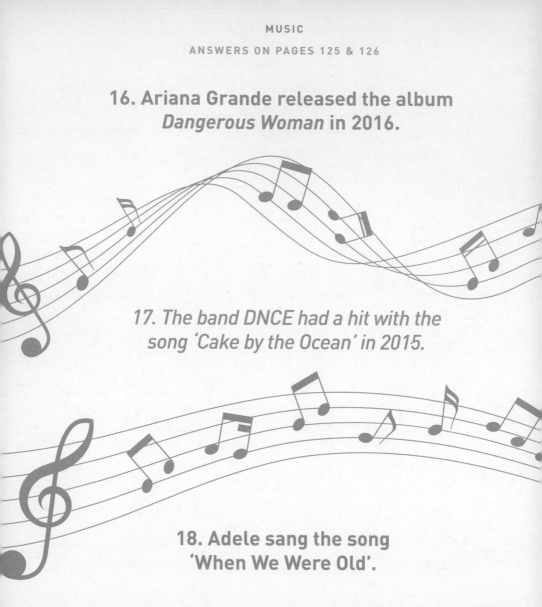

17. The band DNCE had a hit with the
song 'Cake by the Ocean' in 2015.

18. Adele sang the song
'When We Were Old'.

19. Taylor Swift released the album *1989* in 2017.

20. Elvis' surname is Presley.

**21. Calvin Harris released
the song 'This Is What You Came For'.**

22. The Maroon 5 song 'Moves Like Jagger' was a huge hit in 2011.

23. Charlie Puth sang the song 'How Long?' for the soundtrack of the movie Furious 7.

24. John Lennon and Paul McCartney were part of The Beatles.

25. Miley Cyrus released the song 'Malibu'.

26. Julia Michaels' song 'Tissues' was her first single.

27. One Direction's very first official single was 'What Makes You Happy'.

**28. Nick, Joe and Kevin Jonas
were in a Disney movie.**

*29. Michael Jackson was known
as the King of Rock.*

**30. Jay Z's real first
name is Shawn.**

31. The band ABBA came from Sweden.

32. Pink's song 'What About Us' is from the album Beautiful Trauma.

33. One of Katy Perry's most famous songs is called 'Lion'.

Answers

1. **True.** *They were Harry Styles, Zayn Malik, Niall Horan, Liam Payne and Louis Tomlinson.*
2. **True.** *She released it in 2017.*
3. **False.** *His name is Luke.*
4. **False.** *It was called* Thank You.

5. **True.** *The song is off his album* Divide.
6. **True.** *It was her sixth album.*
7. **False.** *It's 'Uptown Funk'.*
8. **False.** *It's 'Just stop your crying'.*
9. **True.** *His songs include 'There's Nothing Holdin' Me Back' and 'In My Blood'.*
10. **False.** *It's Stefani.*
11. **False.** *It was called 'God's Plan'.*
12. **True.** *She was born in the city of Adelaide.*
13. **False.** *Justin Timberlake sang the song.*
14. **False.** *They released it in 2017.*
15. **True.** *She released the song in 2017.*
16. **True.** *One of the hit songs from that album was 'Into You'.*

Answers

17. **True.** *The lead singer of the band is Joe Jonas.*

18. **False.** *The song is 'When We Were Young'.*

19. **False.** *She released* Reputation *in 2017. The album* 1989 *was released in 2014.*

20. **True.** *Elvis Presley was one of the most successful singers ever.*

21. **True.** *Rihanna sang the lyrics.*

22. **True.** *Maroon 5 is an American pop/rock band.*

23. **False.** *His song 'See You Again' was on the soundtrack to that movie.*

24. **True.** *The Beatles was one of the most popular bands ever.*

25. **True.** *She released it in 2017.*

26. **False.** *The song is 'Issues'.*

27. **False.** *The song was called 'What Makes You Beautiful'.*

28. **True.** *The movie was called* Camp Rock, *released in 2008.*

29. **False.** *He was the King of Pop.*

30. **True.** *His full name is Shawn Corey Carter.*

31. **True.** *The band split up back in 1982.*

32. **True.** *She released the album in 2017.*

33. **False.** *It's called 'Roar'.*

Collect
them all

MINDGAMES

WOULD YOU RATHER?

A game of questions & possibilities

MINDGAMES

What If?

A game of questions & possibilities

MINDGAMES

TRUE or FALSE?

A game of questions & possibilities

MINDGAMES

Dare

A game of questions & possibilities